SEVEN STEPS TO INNER POWER

BY

GRANDMASTER
TAE YUN KIM

SEVEN
STEPS
TO
INNER
POWER

A MARTIAL ARTS MASTER REVEALS
HER SECRETS FOR DYNAMIC LIVING

BY

GRANDMASTER
TAE YUN KIM

My Dear Adam,
You are One of a Kind!
You are Creative Energy!

NORTHSTAR

He Can Do, She Can Do, Why Not Me!

Love, Tae Yun Kim

Table of Contents

Chapter 4 Becoming One With Your Silent Master

Chapter 5 Your Silent Master in Action

Chapter 6 Communing With Your Silent Master

Introduction

Who are you? What do you want to become? Where are you today?
What have you accomplished or failed to accomplish? Do you have
the career you want, the relationships you want? Do you like who
you are? Are you happy? Have you realized your dreams and goals?
Do you have a yearning to realize a deeper sense of joy, peace, and
purpose?

This workbook, based on my book *Seven Steps to Inner Power*, will
help you answer these questions. If you don't like the answers, this
workbook will help you change them! Are you ready? Get your
pencil out and be prepared to chart a vast new territory for yourself.

There are no right or wrong answers to the exercises. Your journey
and the things you discover along the way are your own. The
exercises are intended to stimulate you into a greater awareness
and appreciation of your true self, that quiet voice of wisdom
within you, whom I call your Silent Master.

Alongside each exercise are the passages from *Seven Steps to Inner
Power* upon which the exercises are based. Although these
passages make the workbook able to stand on its own, I recommend
that you keep a copy of Seven Steps to Inner Power handy so you
can take in the full meaning of each exercise.

In this introduction, you will examine your life as it is now: what
got you to this point, where you want to go, what is holding you
back, and what is most important to you. These exercises will
prepare you for a deeper search in the following chapters.

Your birthright is serenity, love, freedom, and the power that you
possess as an essential part of this universe. Claim it! Celebrate
every living breath, every moment. My love will be with you
always.

Grandmaster Tae Yun Kim

Breaking Barriers

*"Blade of grass fluttering
    in the wind
Breaking rock,
Within."*

"Can you imagine your hand going through a brick, breaking it to pieces? Can you imagine it going through a stack of ten bricks? Maybe you think this is an impossible accomplishment for yourself or for anyone. I assure you it's not... What I can teach you will enable you to break not only bricks but also the harder barriers that may be blocking happiness and fulfillment in your life."

Have you ever observed a blade of grass that grows through the cement or the small tree that grows on solid rock? Look carefully. It is the cement or the rock that cracks. What obstacles in your life right now feel like rocks weighing you down?

_____

_____

_____

_____

_____

Keep these in mind as you work through the exercises in this book. The purpose of this book is to help you break through!

Identify the thoughts that you have had that shaped your life in some way. What thoughts have propelled you to accomplish what you wanted?

☯ This morning?

_____

_____

☯ This week?

_____

_____

☯ This year?

_____

_____

☯ In your life?

_____

_____

_____

What is blocking your true happiness and fulfillment at this moment? Answer these 10 questions.

☯ How do you spend your time?

_____

_____

_____

☯ Are you happy?

_____

_____

_____

☯ Do you like getting up in the morning?

_____

_____

_____

☯ Do you have a purpose in your life?

_____

_____

_____

_____

❂ How would you describe your health?

_____

_____

_____

❂ Are you comfortable with your physical being?

_____

_____

_____

❂ Do you know what is important to you?

_____

_____

_____

❂ Do you have enough income to support your desired lifestyle?

_____

_____

_____

❂ How is your financial health?

_____

_____

_____

❂ What areas would you most like to improve?

_____

_____

_____

How Satisfied Are You?

	Very Satisfied	Somewhat Satisfied	Not Satisfied
Career	❑	❑	❑
Health	❑	❑	❑
Fitness	❑	❑	❑
Money	❑	❑	❑
Purpose	❑	❑	❑
Relationships	❑	❑	❑
Spirituality	❑	❑	❑
Values	❑	❑	❑

Directions: Place a check mark in each appropriate category. Check your current feelings about your level of satisfaction within each area.

What barrier is blocking you from achieving complete satisfaction in each of these areas? How do you feel about your current level of satisfaction? Do you think you can change it?

"Is it not your thought that moves you throughout your life?"

_____

_____

_____

_____

_____

_____

_____

_____

"Like the fabric of a tapestry, one thread will always lead to many others... Has anything worthwhile ever been accomplished without effort?"

Name ten areas in which you have accomplished what you wanted.

1. _____

2. _____

3. _____

4. _____

5. _____

6. _____

7. _____

8. _____

9. _____

10. _____

Name ten areas in which you have failed to accomplish what you wanted.

1. _____

2. _____

3. _____

4. _____

5. _____

6. _____

7. _____

8. _____

9. _____

10. _____

Write down the three things you most want to accomplish in life. Do not limit yourself to things you think are "realistic." Be honest with yourself. You can't fool life, and you don't want to fool yourself.

Life Purpose

1. _____

_____

_____

_____

2. _____

_____

_____

_____

3. _____

_____

_____

_____

Of these, which is the most important? Why?

_____

_____

_____

_____

_____

_____

_____

Life Time Line

The time line below represents your life. The beginning mark indicates the beginning of your life. Begin working with the time line by placing a mark where you think your life is today in the overall span you expect to live. Then go back and mark each major event of your life that indicates the transitions that have shaped your life.

Birth

"People and events can shape someone for good or bad. But you alone have power over these things, more power than you realize... What I discovered was that how I dealt with circumstances was much more important than the circumstances themselves."

Describe the one experience from the Life Time Line that had the most influence on your life or that you learned the most from.

_____

_____

_____

_____

_____

_____

_____

_____

_____

_____

_____

If you could change anything you have done in your life so far, what would that be?

_____

_____

_____

_____

_____

_____

What would you like to do differently from now on?

_____

_____

_____

_____

_____

_____

1   *Your Silent Master*

THE POWER OF YOUR TRUE SELF

In this chapter, you will begin to discover your true self and the vast creative potential you have.

What roles do you play? What activities do you engage in? How do you see yourself interacting with others? How have you learned these roles growing up, and how well do they reflect your true self?

Review yesterday and today in your mind. Have you been the friend? The parent? The child? The spouse? The athlete? The boss? The employee? The life of the party? The nobody? Think about the positive and negative personality traits that you have developed to fulfill each role.

The Question... Who Am I?

"This question is unique to human consciousness, certainly fundamental, sometimes difficult, but absolutely essential if you wish to express your fullest potential in life."

Role   Characteristics

1. _____ _____

2. _____ _____

3. _____ _____

4. _____ _____

5. _____ _____

6. _____ _____

7. _____ _____

8. _____ _____

9. _____ _____

10. _____ _____

"The truth is, you are exactly where you are because of the way you answered, 'Who Am I?' Why? Because how you answer the question determines what choices you make for yourself moment to moment every day of your life."

Playing roles is often necessary, but these roles can hide who you really are. Answer each of these questions honestly.

☯ What do you want to become?

_____

_____

☯ Where are you today?

_____

_____

"Suppose I were to tell you that you are aware of only a limited portion of yourself, that you may not have yet discovered your self, your true self, and that you have yet to touch upon an enormous creative power within you that can reshape your life completely."

☯ What have you accomplished or failed to accomplish?

_____

_____

☯ Do you have what you want?

_____

_____

☯ Do you like who you are?

_____

_____

☯ Are you happy?

_____

_____

☯ Have you realized your dreams and goals?

_____

_____

If you were to write an autobiography, what would you say on the last page about what you have done and where you are going?

_____

_____

_____

_____

_____

If you were to write a sequel autobiography decades from now in your maturity, what would it say on the last page?

_____

_____

_____

_____

_____

_____

What would you want it to say?

_____

_____

_____

_____

_____

_____

"If you're holding dreams that feel so true, yet somehow out of reach, if you feel unfulfilled, frustrated, alienated, empty, if you feel you haven't done what you want, if there is more that you desire, more that you want to accomplish, if you feel that even though your life is satisfactory in most respects, you nevertheless have a yearning to realize a deeper sense of joy, peace, and purpose, it is time to extend your vision of who you are."

"No matter who you are, no matter where you are, no matter what obstacles and limitations exist around you at this moment, you can change your life, your health, and your state of mind completely. You can decide who you want to become."

If you had only five days to live, how would you spend them?

_____

_____

_____

_____

_____

_____

How do you want to change your life? List ten ways.

1. _____

2. _____

3. _____

4. _____

5. _____

6. _____

7. _____

8. _____

9. _____

10. _____

How much time in your life do you think you will have to complete each item on the list above? Do you know for sure?

_____

_____

_____

_____

Your Silent Master Consciousness

How much have you taken control of your life and been the driving force behind your choices?

Rate your satisfaction profile.

"When you find your Silent Master within yourself, you take control of your life... Before, you may have been drifting through life; now you are driving through life."

Life Power Profile

Rate your own level of satisfaction within each power area of your life.

Do I feel I can...	Rarely		Sometimes		Most of the Time	
Overcome mental and physical limits	1	2	3	4	5	6
Harmonize and change conflict	1	2	3	4	5	6
Create and achieve goals	1	2	3	4	5	6
Feel peace and joy regardless of circumstances	1	2	3	4	5	6
Be who I really am	1	2	3	4	5	6

On each of the following pages, consider each of the six Silent Master Images, which form the basis of Jung SuWon teaching. As you read each one, visualize what it means to you at the present moment.

I
YOU ARE ONE OF A KIND

Your Silent Master is your Real Self, your original Self. It expresses Itself through your thinking, through true Ideas and Thoughts in your mind. It is your eternal Selfhood that exists apart from your brain (which is a sensory processor only) and the personality traits imposed on you from your environment.

What does Image I mean to you?

_____

_____

_____

_____

_____

_____

_____

_____

_____

II
YOU AND THE LIFE FORCE ARE ONE

Your Silent Master Consciousness was born out of the infinite Life Force creating and animating the Universe. You exist as a part of the Universe; therefore It is the Life Force creating and animating you. It is the power that beats your heart. Because you are this Consciousness, whatever qualities the Life Force possesses, you possess also.

What does Image II mean to you?

_____

_____

_____

_____

_____

_____

_____

_____

_____

III
YOUR THOUGHTS CREATE REALITY

Your Silent Master Consciousness knows Itself to be immaterial in substance, but It also takes form (manifests) as your physical body and the material world around you. Thus, you may describe yourself as being both immaterial (spiritual) and material (physical) at the same time.

What does Image III mean to you?

_____

_____

_____

_____

_____

_____

_____

_____

_____

IV
YOU ARE CREATIVE ENERGY

Your Silent Master knows Itself as the Source of mental, emotional, and material Energy—your Energy, which you are free to utilize and control in creating what you desire. Therefore, you are a Co-Creator, cooperating with the Life Force of the Universe to shape yourself and the world around you.

What does Image IV mean to you?

_____

_____

_____

_____

_____

_____

_____

_____

_____

V
YOU HAVE THE POWER TO FULFILL YOUR DREAMS

Your Silent Master is completely aware, infinitely Intelligent, and ready to give you all the insight, information, and direction you need to fulfill your dreams, ambitions, and goals. In fact, this Consciousness is the Source of all your true desires.

What does Image V mean to you?

_____

_____

_____

_____

_____

_____

_____

_____

_____

VI
YOU ARE COMPLETE, PEACEFUL, AND FULFILLED

Your Silent Master expresses completeness, fulfillment, harmony, peace, joy, and love, and imparts these qualities to everything It creates.

What does Image VI mean to you?

_____

_____

_____

_____

_____

_____

_____

_____

_____

Your Silent Master thinks in unlimited ways. For example:

When you think:	Your Silent Master thinks:
I am a failure	*I have mental and physical strength to act and achieve.*
I am afraid	*I have no fear because I am the source of all real power.*
I am sick	*I am eternally well and whole, and I can prove it.*

What are some of the limitations you often think you have? What would your Silent Master say?

What You Think	What Your Silent Master Thinks
_____	_____
_____	_____
_____	_____
_____	_____
_____	_____
_____	_____
_____	_____
_____	_____
_____	_____

You can learn about who you are and what you have become over the years when you understand how your earliest ideas about yourself were formed.

Write down five positive things your parents said about you that shaped who you believe you are.

1. _____

2. _____

3. _____

4. _____

5. _____

The Distraction...

"As a child you couldn't alienate the people who were responsible for your physical and emotional survival, so you went along with them the best you could. Perhaps you resisted certain concepts about yourself along the way, but for the most part, you accepted what others had to say about you. And you acted accordingly."

Write down five negative things your parents said about you that shaped who you believe you are.

1. _____

2. _____

3. _____

4. _____

5. _____

"You may have learned that the path of least resistance was to do what was expected of you, do what you were told, not be too different, and not to argue with the system. Notice that although the system was designed to give you a share of safety and security, it did not guarantee happiness, or fulfillment, or freedom— or any of the things that make life truly worth living."

List five ways that you "went along" with what others (family, friends, teachers, etc.) wanted you to do.

1. _____

2. _____

3. _____

4. _____

5. _____

"Now many of the choices you make— even your most important choices, such as a spouse or career—are really 'their' choices."

Have you made major decisions in your life that were wrong for you because you were trying to please others? If so, list them.

_____

_____

_____

_____

_____

_____

The big questions when we were children was, "What do you want to be when you grow up?" Take a moment below to visualize your childhood dreams. What did you want to be when you grew up?

_____

_____

_____

_____

How does this compare to where you are now? Did you give up on a dream, or did you find and fulfill one?

_____

_____

_____

_____

_____

_____

Your Silent Master is your original self still waiting to be born. It can help you to become who you want to be. It can help you learn to overcome, to grow, to find your power and purpose, and to live it!

The Solution

"The rewards of becoming new are great."

◐ How do you want to change?

_____

_____

_____

◐ What discomforts are you willing to experience and conquer?

_____

_____

_____

"Does not the small fish that hatches upstream face great risks in swimming to the much larger ocean where it will grow big and strong?"

◐ What obstacles and limitations do you want to attack and eliminate?

_____

_____

_____

◐ What new opportunities and new challenges do you envision?

_____

_____

_____

2 *Seeking Your Silent Master*

TAPPING INTO YOUR POWER

In this chapter, you will learn how you can change your life by changing your way of thinking.

The power of the Silent Master within you is the power of right thinking, and the difference between a limited you and an unlimited you begins with your attitude and state of mind.

"How do you bring forth your Silent Master in your thinking right now?"

Are you aware of your thoughts? For the next 5 minutes, write down every thought you have—even the incomplete ones, the fragmented ones, the silly ones, the unpleasant ones, the thoughts that ramble. Let your mind flow from one thought to another naturally. Write quickly. Do not worry about the form—just capture as many of your thoughts as you can.

_____

_____

_____

_____

_____

_____

_____

_____

"The first step in taking charge of your life is to learn to take charge of your thinking."

How would you describe your overall state of mind during this exercise?

❑ extremely positive

❑ very positive

❑ somewhat positive

❑ neutral

❑ somewhat negative

❑ very negative

❑ extremely negative

"When you look at everything you have manifested in your life now, you're looking at a picture of the quality of your thinking and feeling."

What percentage of the time were you thinking about what is really important to you?

_____

0% - - 25% - - 50% - - 75% - - 100%

_____

How much time did you spend thinking about the past, present, and future?

Past: _____%

Present: _____%

Future: _____%

Remember Silent Master Image III:

Demonstrating the Law of Manifestation

YOUR THOUGHTS CREATE REALITY

Your Silent Master Consciousness knows Itself to be immaterial in substance, but It also takes form (manifests) as your physical body and the material world around you. Thus, you may describe yourself as being both immaterial (spiritual) and material (physical) at the same time.

List the thoughts and beliefs you have about the following aspects of your life:

Your Body

Examples: "I am graceful." "I am not athletic." "I am attractive."

_____

_____

_____

Your Mind

Examples: "I am intellectual." "I am not good at math."

_____

_____

_____

Your Personality and Emotions

Examples: "I am shy." "I am a fighter." "If I cry, it shows I am weak."

_____

_____

_____

Your Talents

Examples: "I can't sing." "I can fix anything on wheels."

_____

_____

_____

Success and Career

Examples: "I'm not educated enough." "It's a jungle out there."

_____

_____

_____

Other People

Examples: "I don't understand people." "Children are naturally selfish." "Women can't be trusted." "Men are overgrown boys."

_____

_____

_____

Relationships

Examples: "I am not lovable." "They only like me for my looks." "Real friends are hard to find."

_____

_____

_____

"Everything external in life was first internal in thought, so no permanent change can come about merely by attempting to fix or rearrange external conditions."

Now that you have looked at some of your basic beliefs, examine the following areas of your life.

Your Body

Are you healthy? Are you overweight or underweight? Do you exercise?

_____

_____

_____

Your Mind

Does your job require an education? Are you responsible for making decisions? Are you eager to learn new things?

_____

_____

_____

Your Personality and Emotions

Are you calm, or do you often get moody? Do you bounce back when difficulties arise?

_____

_____

_____

Your Talents

What kinds of things can you do that are not common? What are you most afraid to do?

_____

_____

_____

Success and Career

What profession are you in? How much do you earn? How far have you progressed?

_____

_____

_____

Other People and Relationships

Are you happy with your significant other? Do you find yourself in the same kinds of conflicts with people over and over again? Do you find it hard to maintain good relationships with people?

_____

_____

_____

_____

_____

Compare your beliefs and your current situation. Do you see how they relate?

_____

_____

_____

_____

_____

_____

_____

_____

"When we see the symptoms of something wrong in our lives, we usually try to get rid of the symptoms instead of getting rid of the mental condition that's causing the symptoms."

Changing Your Beliefs

List the things in your life that you most want to change. List what you currently believe in that area, then list what your new belief needs to be to bring about the change you desire. For example:

To change	*I must stop believing that*	*And start believing that*
my job to a managerial position	I am shy	I have the ability to work with people

To change	**I must stop believing that**	**And start believing that**
_____	_____	_____
_____	_____	_____
_____	_____	_____
_____	_____	_____
_____	_____	_____
_____	_____	_____
_____	_____	_____
_____	_____	_____
_____	_____	_____
_____	_____	_____
_____	_____	_____
_____	_____	_____
_____	_____	_____

How would you describe yourself? Do you like yourself the way you are?

_____

_____

_____

_____

_____

_____

_____

_____

_____

Identify Your Fears and Weaknesses and Conquer Them

"We have certain qualities called 'strengths' that tend to lead us into greater harmony and peace; and we have other qualities called 'weaknesses' that tend to undermine or sabotage the good we try to do."

List ten strengths you have.

1. _____

2. _____

3. _____

4. _____

5. _____

6. _____

7. _____

8. _____

9. _____

10. _____

"Your strengths alone are big enough to share with everyone and big enough to confront any situation."

"Look clinically at your strengths and weaknesses. Don't make value judgments. You must have the courage to operate on yourself with the same objectivity to rid yourself of that which can harm you. What is the result? You will feel a sense of peace because you are well and whole... When you find your strengths, decide to keep them, but do not become overly confident or egotistical. When you find your weaknesses, determine to eliminate them, but do not fall in a mire of depression, dejection, or self-condemnation."

List ten weaknesses you have.

1. _____

2. _____

3. _____

4. _____

5. _____

6. _____

7. _____

8. _____

9. _____

10. _____

Which list was harder to compose? Your strengths or weaknesses?

_____

_____

Why?

_____

_____

_____

_____

_____

In the space below, list again the ten weaknesses you perceive in yourself as well as the way you will know you are free from them.

Weakness   Freedom

1. _____ _____

2. _____ _____

3. _____ _____

4. _____ _____

5. _____ _____

6. _____ _____

7. _____ _____

8. _____ _____

9. _____ _____

10. _____ _____

"How do you know when you have eliminated your weaknesses? When you are no longer dominated by them. For instance, if a former alcoholic refuses to drink, but is afraid to look at a bottle, to some extent she is still being held by the disease... When you no longer fear you'll fall prey to your weaknesses, you feel your true strength."

List five weaknesses in others that you especially dislike and ask yourself, "Am I afraid of this weakness?"

Weakness that I dislike in others:

Weakness that I dislike in others:	Am I afraid of this weakness?	
_____	Yes	No
_____	Yes	No
_____	Yes	No
_____	Yes	No
_____	Yes	No
_____	Yes	No
_____	Yes	No
_____	Yes	No

"During the process of self-analysis, you may notice that others have weaknesses you don't have. A word of warning: Perhaps another person does indeed have some weaknesses you don't have. But if you find yourself reacting, especially reacting emotionally to this person's weakness, chances are 99.9% certain that you also have that weakness. Look closely at things you hate in others and ask yourself this question: 'Am I afraid of this weakness?'"

"These are just a few weak, powerless states of mind to be conquered. When you find yourself reacting with compassion to these characteristics in another or in yourself, you'll know you are well on your way to conquering them. Why? Because compassion is one of the qualities of your Silent Master."

Which of the following "powerless states" do you need to conquer? Circle those that apply.

Anger	Fear	Resentment	Laziness
Despair	Worry	Pessimism	Selfishness
Revenge	Sarcasm	Depression	Illness

Each weakness has an opposing strength. Look carefully at the weaknesses listed below and match them to the list of strengths. There are no wrong answers. Match them according to your feelings. Get in touch with your original self.

"Weaknesses are not part of your original self. By replacing your weaknesses with strengths, you've done everything you need to do to conquer these enemies of your well-being."

Weakness	**Strength**
Anger	Action
Sadness	Courage
Misery	Calmness
Self-Doubt	Energy
Stubbornness	Forgiveness
Hurt	Happiness
Tiredness	Health
Depression	Joy
Laziness	Love
Bitterness	Selflessness
Self-Hatred	Self-Love
Panic	Serenity
Conflict	Support
Selfishness	Willingness

List ten important mistakes that you perceive you have made—mistakes in judgment, what you said or did, how you thought about something, etc. Do not judge yourself or the mistakes as being wrong or right—just observe and note what you could have done instead.

Mistake	Alternative Action
1. _____	_____
2. _____	_____
3. _____	_____
4. _____	_____
5. _____	_____
6. _____	_____
7. _____	_____
8. _____	_____
9. _____	_____
10. _____	_____

Review the mistakes you listed. How did you feel about each mistake?

1. _____

2. _____

3. _____

4. _____

5. _____

6. _____

7. _____

8. _____

9. _____

10. _____

Learn from Your Mistakes

"Mistakes...are part of a natural feedback system in learning a task or accomplishing a goal. That's all."

"We tend to hide our mistakes because we think we cannot be weak. So when we do make a mistake, we attempt to move on quickly, to cover it up. We will excuse it, justify it, cover it up... anything but look long and hard at it."

"What is the worst thing that can happen if you make a mistake? You will have to abandon that course of action and take another, which means, in short, a lot of work... You may have to be creative. You may have to expend energy in thinking, evaluating, planning. You may have to resist emotions such as despair, futility, rejection, and fear."

"If you are mentally lazy, making mistakes will be one of the best excuses you have for giving up... What a senseless waste that would be. Why expect so little out of life?"

"When you find yourself joyfully moving from one situation to another, using mistakes for learning, growing, and improving, your Silent Master is beginning to operate in your life."

What were you trying to accomplish when you made each mistake? Was this accomplishment important?

Accomplishment　　　　　　　　　　　　　　Important?

1. _____　Yes　No

2. _____　Yes　No

3. _____　Yes　No

4. _____　Yes　No

5. _____　Yes　No

6. _____　Yes　No

7. _____　Yes　No

8. _____　Yes　No

9. _____　Yes　No

10. _____　Yes　No

We have the Ability to Do...

"The purpose of the third rule of mental conduct is to emphasize how you limit yourself by yourself. You limit your thinking, with your thinking. This rule tells you to wake up, open up, expand your expectations, and realize you can achieve and produce whatever you can think."

We have the Ability to Do, the Capacity to Act, and the Capability to Perform and Produce.
Read Silent Master Images II and IV carefully:

II
YOU AND THE LIFE FORCE ARE ONE

Your Silent Master Consciousness was born out of the infinite Life Force creating and animating the Universe. You exist as a part of the Universe; therefore It is the Life Force creating and animating you. It is the power that beats your heart. Because you are this Consciousness, whatever qualities the Life Force possesses, you possess also.

IV
YOU ARE CREATIVE ENERGY

*Your Silent Master knows Itself as the
Source of mental, emotional, and
material Energy— your Energy, which you
are free to utilize and control in creating
what you desire. Therefore, you are a Co-
Creator, cooperating with the Life Force
of the Universe to shape yourself and the
world around you.*

Do you have a secret wish that you have always thought was not possible? Or do you have an ambitious goal that requires tremendous effort to reach? What is this wish or goal?

_____

_____

_____

_____

_____

*"Does that sound too
audacious? Whatever
you can think? What is
it that you really want?
This is not an invitation
to be frivolous in your
thinking. If anything,
this is a warning to be
careful what you think...
There is some truth in
the expression, 'Be
careful what you wish
for; you might get it.' "*

List some smaller goals or conditions that would have to be met in order to make your secret wish or ambitious goal come true.

1. _____

2. _____

3. _____

4. _____

5. _____

6. _____

7. _____

8. _____

9. _____

10. _____

Are any of the smaller goals or conditions impossible? Why?

_____

_____

_____

_____

_____

Review your thoughts about yourself that you listed in the first exercise under "Demonstrating the Law of Manifestation." Compare these thoughts to your reason why your wish or goal is impossible. Do you see how your view of yourself determines what you think you can achieve?

_____

_____

_____

What are some examples of thoughts that once were considered outrageous, and now have become reality? For example: "Walking on the moon." Think also of people who conquered a physical limitation, such as Helen Keller or Christopher Reeve.

1. _____

2. _____

3. _____

4. _____

5. _____

6. _____

7. _____

8. _____

9. _____

10. _____

Is your "impossible" wish or goal more outrageous than these once outrageous thoughts?

_____

_____

_____

Resisting Negative Thoughts

Can you see that you can be your own worst enemy by thinking negatively about yourself? Again, review your thoughts about yourself that you listed in the first exercise under "Demonstrating the Law of Manifestation." What are some ways in which you are getting in your own way?

_____

_____

_____

_____

_____

_____

When was the last time someone influenced your thought? What happened?

_____

_____

_____

_____

_____

"We are here to learn to take charge of what we manifest by taking charge of our thinking."

"Others can suggest thoughts to you, but you're the one who accepts or rejects what you entertain in your mind."

Did you accept or reject the other person's influence?

_____

_____

Was it a positive, harmonious thought, or a negative, destructive one?

_____

_____

"When you find yourself uncomfortable with your own negative creations and wanting to change your thinking, you are feeling the presence of your Silent Master."

Remember the last time you entertained negative thoughts in your mind.

How did your body feel?

_____

_____

What were you thinking?

_____

_____

What was in your heart, in your spirit?

_____

_____

What did you say and do?

_____

_____

What would you have done differently?

_____

_____

_____

List five areas that you find in your life that are uncomfortable, unacceptable, limiting, or that make you feel unfulfilled.

1. _____

2. _____

3. _____

4. _____

5. _____

Now re-list these same five areas as you would like them to be, in complete freedom with no limitations. For example, if you wrote that you are unhappy in your current job, you would write something like, "I am happy and fulfilled in my current job."

1. _____

2. _____

3. _____

4. _____

5. _____

List a single short-term goal that you wish to achieve, such as "I want to improve my appearance."

_____

State it again, more specifically this time, for example, "I want to lose weight."

_____

State it again, even more specifically. How much weight do you want to lose? By when?

_____

_____

_____

Have Determination and a Quality Purpose

"When you decide to make a change, achieve a goal, or create something new in your life, you must focus your objective clearly in your mind... Be specific!"

Have you taken steps to reach this goal? What have you done?

_____

_____

"Here's the unfortunate thing about determination: it works only when you want it to."

Did you ever give up on reaching this goal before? After how long?

Weeks: 1   2   3   4

Months: 1   2   3   4   5   6   More

Describe in great detail your secret wish or ambitious goal from the first exercise under "We Have the Ability to Do..." Where are you? What do your surroundings look like? Who are the people around you, and what are you saying to them? What are they saying to you? What do you look like? What do they look like?

_____

_____

_____

_____

_____

_____

_____

_____

_____

_____

_____

To what lengths would you go to achieve this goal if you knew that in the end you would achieve it?

_____

_____

_____

_____

_____

_____

_____

Be A Responsible Creator

Take one of your desires through the steps of looking at the supporting thoughts behind it. List the desire, the supporting thoughts, and whether your thoughts are positive or negative. For example:

My desire is: to lose weight

Beliefs that support my desire: **Positive or Negative?**

   I deserve to feel good about myself.   Pos   Neg

   My health is important.   Pos   Neg

My desire is: _____

Beliefs that support my desire: **Positive or Negative?**

_____ Pos   Neg

_____ Pos   Neg

_____ Pos   Neg

_____ Pos   Neg

_____ Pos   Neg

"Unswerving determination is one of the most important factors in reaching your goal, in reaching any goal. Only you can make determination work for you. And if you use it, your determination will attract to you all the other factors needed for your success."

"Your true desires, those longings for certain goals that feel like a part of you, are given to you from your Silent Master."

"The other aspect of the fourth principle is to have a quality purpose. Because we have such great freedom to create, we must take responsibility to use our power constructively... If you ever have any doubt about whether a certain desire is worthy of your total energy and attention, look at the supporting beliefs behind that desire. That will give you your answer."

Have a Positive Mental Attitude

Your feelings and emotions play a large role in what you manifest or fail to manifest. Together your positive thoughts and feelings create a positive mental attitude. The fifth principle of mental conduct emphasizes how this state of mind is essential for your success.

"Your emotions are your friends when they constructively accompany and support your creative thinking. They are your enemies when they sabotage and conflict with your mental objectives."

"If you think of your thoughts as seeds, think of your emotional environment as soil. Therefore, your positive seeds must be sown in positive soil to grow and flourish."

In the list below, identify which emotions are constructive "friends" and which are sabotaging "enemies."

Anxiety	FRIEND	ENEMY
Belief	FRIEND	ENEMY
Commitment	FRIEND	ENEMY
Depression	FRIEND	ENEMY
Faith	FRIEND	ENEMY
Happiness	FRIEND	ENEMY
Hostility	FRIEND	ENEMY
Hurt	FRIEND	ENEMY
Joy	FRIEND	ENEMY
Love	FRIEND	ENEMY
Peace	FRIEND	ENEMY
Rage	FRIEND	ENEMY
Resentment	FRIEND	ENEMY
Serenity	FRIEND	ENEMY
Fear	FRIEND	ENEMY
Withdrawal	FRIEND	ENEMY

"If you are trying to make a change in your life or achieve a goal, you may need to clear away some negative feelings, even if those feelings are unrelated to your goal."

Go back to the previous question and review the answers you circled. Do you allow sabotaging thoughts to cause conflict in your life? Do you associate in your mind with these "enemies?" Why?

_____

_____

_____

List five areas of your life in which you are trying to make a change (for example, your career).

1. _____

2. _____

3. _____

4. _____

5. _____

Which of these changes has been the most difficult to achieve?

_____

_____

Negative feelings may be in conflict with the change you wish to make. List five negative feelings that you have had lately, even if they seem to have nothing to do with this change. Do not think about them, just write quickly whatever comes to your mind.

1. _____

2. _____

3. _____

4. _____

5. _____

Follow the negative thoughts that you just expressed. Where do they lead you? Do you think they support the change you are trying to make?

_____

_____

_____

_____

"Here is an important point to help you understand your emotions. Emotions don't come out of nowhere; they follow thoughts."

List three negative and positive thoughts you have had today. How did these thoughts make you feel?

Negative Thought   How I Felt

_____   _____

_____   _____

_____   _____

Positive Thought   How I Felt

_____   _____

_____   _____

_____   _____

You Have a Conscious and a Subconscious Mind

"Sometimes your emotions do appear to come out of nowhere, and sometimes they seem to conflict with what you are thinking... What's wrong? The answer is, you may have formed invisible thoughts that are now creating emotions."

Describe a situation in your own life where subconscious programming may be interfering with your conscious choices. What do you want to achieve that is being sabotaged somehow?

_____

_____

_____

_____

_____

"Because you are not aware of what is going on, you don't attack the real cause of the problem; you attack yourself instead."

How does this make you feel?

_____

_____

_____

_____

_____

What do you say to yourself about this?

_____

_____

_____

_____

_____

Help for Your Subconscious Programming

Remember Silent Master Image V:

YOU HAVE THE POWER TO FULFILL YOUR DREAMS

> *Your Silent Master is completely aware,*
> *infinitely Intelligent, and ready to give you*
> *all the insight, information, and direction*
> *you need to fulfill your dreams, ambitions,*
> *and goals. In fact, this Consciousness is*
> *the Source of all your true desires.*

"By simply knowing you have unlimited awareness and intelligence available to you, you can ask for information regarding your obstacle, whatever it may be."

Think of whatever is the most pressing, difficult, or painful area of your life at this moment. What question do you want to ask yourself about this? Write the question below.

_____

_____

_____

"Asking is as simple as mentally posing the question to yourself and expecting the answer to come into your conscious awareness. However long or short a time it takes, the answer will surely come."

Think of five more questions that you want to ask your Silent Master to answer and write them below.

1. _____

2. _____

3. _____

4. _____

5. _____

"Your emotions constantly give you feedback about the quality of your thinking."

Do you have a positive mental attitude? Why or why not? Explain your answer.

_____

_____

_____

_____

_____

_____

_____

_____

_____

How to Deal with Negative Emotions

When you feel negative, first acknowledge that you feel negative.

Which emotions do you find most unpleasant or hard to admit to?

_____

_____

_____

_____

_____

_____

"It may seem overly simplistic to simply acknowledge your negative emotions, but you'd be surprised how often you refuse to acknowledge that you're feeling angry or depressed... There will always be some deeper, covert manifestation of ignored emotions—such as developing a headache instead of expressing your anger—and as an effective emotion-dodger, you'll say the physical symptom is due to some other cause."

Do you find that you frequently have minor physical complaints? What are they? Do you think they could be suppressed emotions?

_____

_____

_____

_____

_____

_____

_____

Do emotions sometimes erupt as if from out of nowhere? Describe what happens. How long do you find that these emotions have been buried?

_____

_____

_____

_____

_____

_____

_____

After you acknowledge the presence of the negative feeling, next remember that you have three options. Choose the third option and avoid the first two. The options are:

- ☯ Carving in Wood or Stone

- ☯ Writing in Sand

- ☯ Writing in Water

"You may have felt so righteously justified in feeling your negative feelings that you accepted them and had no intention of letting them go. But whom does this really affect? It hurts only you."

Have you carved some emotions in wood or stone? For example, do you hold a grudge against someone? Describe the situation and your feelings.

_____

_____

When you think about this carved-in emotion, how does your body feel?

_____

_____

How does this carved-in emotion hinder you in achieving your goals?

_____

_____

"Negative emotions that are held until something external happens to stimulate them or change them are like writing in sand. We haven't determined to keep them, but we haven't determined to release them."

Have you carved some emotions in sand? For example, have you ever said, "I'll be angry as long as _____"? Describe the situation and your feelings.

_____

_____

_____

_____

Do you still feel this way?   No   Yes

If no, what happened to change your feelings?

_____

_____

If yes, how does this emotion hinder you in achieving your goals?

_____

_____

Writing in water means you acknowledge a negative emotion but immediately let it go. Sometimes this is hard to do. Why?

_____

_____

_____

"Do not allow negative emotions to reside in your consciousness for any amount of time or to become permanent."

Do you sometimes enjoy your negative emotional states? Be honest. What are some of the payoffs? For example: "When I'm depressed, my husband/wife pays more attention to me."

1. _____

2. _____

3. _____

4. _____

5. _____

Positive Emotions Come From Your Real Self

Remember Silent Master Image VI:

YOU ARE COMPLETE, PEACEFUL, AND FULFILLED

Your Silent Master expresses completeness, fulfillment, harmony, peace, joy, and love, and imparts these qualities to everything It creates.

How do you want to change your attitude to make it more positive?

_____

_____

_____

_____

"If you truly find yourself growing more and more uncomfortable with your negative emotions, if they are annoying distractions to this little flame of peace and well-being starting to glow within you, if you find yourself wanting to nurture even the smallest, most quiet feeling of self-appreciation, if you find yourself wanting, really wanting, to be happy within yourself, you are feeling your Silent Master."

3 *Three Tools of the Jung SuWon Warrior*

BALANCE - AWARENESS - VISUALIZATION

In this chapter, you will learn how balance, awareness, and visualization can help you stay on your journey. The knowledge of Balance will be the armor you wear so you can travel fearlessly through any experience life brings to you. Awareness will be the shield you use to deflect that which you do not need or want. Visualization will be the sword you use to cut through worn, outmoded, or negative forms to make room for the new.

One of nature's manifestations is a great fundamental principle of the Universe: namely, Unity through Polarity. This principle is depicted in oriental philosophies, including Jung SuWon, as the yin-yang symbol.

Balance

List five things or forces that illustrate this concept of yin (female, quiet, passive) and yang (male, strong, active) existing together in unity and balance. Be bold about your thoughts and look to nature for your answers.

1. _____

2. _____

3. _____

4. _____

5. _____

"The circle taken as a whole also tells us that the Life Force of the Universe operates via two equal and opposite forces, which manifest in some form on every level of our life experience."

How do you experience the balancing of opposite forces in your life in the following areas?

Physically:

_____

_____

_____

Emotionally:

_____

_____

_____

Mentally:

_____

_____

_____

Spiritually:

_____

_____

_____

Do you create harmony in your own life with cycles of rest and activity? Is it in balance? Why or why not? Explain your answer.

_____

_____

_____

_____

_____

Can you identify the times of "yin" and "yang" in the pace of and activities in your own life? What does each feel like? Which do you prefer?

_____

_____

_____

_____

_____

_____

Remember Silent Master Image II:

YOU AND THE LIFE FORCE ARE ONE

Your Silent Master Consciousness was born out of the infinite Life Force creating and animating the Universe. You exist as a part of the Universe; therefore It is the Life Force creating and animating you. It is the power that beats your heart. Because you are this Consciousness, whatever qualities the Life Force possesses, you possess also.

Now that you know about yin and yang forces, how do you see yourself in connection with the Universe?

_____

_____

_____

_____

_____

"Because the yin-yang symbol describes the Life Force of the Universe, it also describes your Silent Master Consciousness, which contains all the qualities, all the potential of both yin and yang."

What are situations in which you would typically express a yang action? Write three in the first column below.

Yang Action   Balancing Action

_____   _____

_____   _____

_____   _____

What are situations in which you would typically express a yin action? Write three in the first column below.

Yin Action   Balancing Action

_____   _____

_____   _____

_____   _____

Go back to the previous two questions and in the second column list ways you could balance out your actions.

What did you learn about yourself?

_____

_____

"Perhaps the most obvious manifestation of yin and yang in action is change. The motion of these two forces in the world are seen in rhythms of change such as day and night, the ebb and flow of the tides, the changing of seasons, birth and death, death and regeneration, seed and harvest."

What times of the day do you feel...

Most energetic: _____

Least energetic: _____

Most inspired and creative: _____

Most organized: _____

Name five situations where you have experienced the ebb and flow and rhythm of these forces in your life.

1. _____

2. _____

3. _____

4. _____

5. _____

Does understanding this concept in more depth help you have a different perception of things that have happened in the past? Why?

_____

_____

_____

_____

_____

_____

_____

Describe a cycle you feel you're within right now.

_____

_____

_____

_____

_____

_____

_____

When you see where you exist in connection to the whole cycle, does this give you a different perception of your circumstances? How?

_____

_____

_____

_____

_____

_____

"Just because that seed is present does not mean it will always automatically develop. In the cycle of seed and harvest, for example, the harvest does not arrive automatically. The farmer must work the land, plant the seeds, and provide the water. When you desire a change, you must do the work of choosing to bring about the change and support your choice with appropriate actions."

What kind of action or change could you bring into your life to support your goals?

_____

_____

_____

_____

_____

_____

"Decrease and emptiness are not necessarily negative states. They may be serving a purpose: to take away that which may be standing in your way of greater good."

Can you think of a time when you were experiencing something that seemed tragic or traumatic only to find later that it opened doors to better things around the corner? Describe the situation.

_____

_____

_____

_____

_____

What did you learn from this experience?

_____

_____

_____

_____

_____

_____

_____

"There is another law associated with the laws of change: Unending Progress. This law affirms that the whole purpose of change, the whole purpose of continuous cycles of yin and yang, is to take you higher, to make you grow, to give you more of what will lead you to a truer expression of your Real Self."

Do you think you are afraid of change? Why or why not?

_____

_____

_____

_____

"By letting go and listening to your Silent Master, all change should lead you into greater good. That is the purpose of change and the purpose of life."

What are some instances when you felt that you made a wrong move?

_____

_____

_____

_____

_____

_____

_____

Awareness

"Your Silent Master Consciousness knows when a yin or yang action is called for to create balance. Yet, how often have you found yourself making the wrong move, increasing discord rather than eliminating it? You may even have had moments where you said,'If only I had listened to myself, I wouldn't have done that.'"

"You may not be aware of it, but your Silent Master Consciousness appears to speak to you very quietly sometimes, through a faculty we call intuition."

Did your intuition tell you to do something different? What would you have done instead if you had listened to your intuition?

_____

_____

_____

_____

_____

_____

_____

"How can you make your mind like a pool of still, clean water, undisturbed by turbulent surface thoughts, free from polluting feelings and emotions, so that the light of your Silent Master Consciousness travels easily into your awareness?"

Repeat the following exercise from Chapter 2. For the next 5 minutes, write down every thought you have—even the incomplete ones, the fragmented ones, the silly ones, the unpleasant ones, the thoughts that ramble. Let your mind flow from one thought to another naturally. Write quickly. Do not worry about the form— just capture as many of your thoughts as you can.

_____

_____

_____

_____

_____

_____

_____

_____

_____

How would you describe your overall state of mind during this exercise?

- ❑ extremely positive

- ❑ very positive

- ❑ somewhat positive

- ❑ neutral

- ❑ somewhat negative

- ❑ very negative

- ❑ extremely negative

"How can you hear your Silent Master this very moment if your mind is occupied with yesterday's resentment? Or today's panic? Or tomorrow's anticipation? Or with fear, worry, and anger?"

What percentage of the time were you thinking about what is really important to you?

0% - - 25% - - 50% - - 75% - - 100%

How much time did you spend thinking about the past, present, and future?

Past: _____%

Present: _____%

Future: _____%

"Your Silent Master speaks to you always in the present moment, because Now is all there is. Therefore, Now is where reality is, and Now is where the creative moment is."

Now that you have taken a moment to listen to your thoughts right now, remember that your thoughts create reality. What kind of reality are you creating right now?

_____

_____

_____

_____

_____

What is something in the past or future that you often think about?

_____

_____

_____

_____

_____

_____

Do you gain anything by thinking about this over and over? If not, what can you do to let go and move on?

_____

_____

_____

_____

_____

"When you can seize control of the Now moment, you take intelligent control of your life."

What kind of reality do you want to create?

_____

_____

_____

_____

_____

_____

Remember Silent Master Images I and III:

Visualization

I
YOU ARE ONE OF A KIND

*Your Silent Master is your Real Self, your
original Self. It expresses Itself through
your thinking, through true Ideas and
Thoughts in your mind...*

III
YOUR THOUGHTS CREATE REALITY

*Your Silent Master Consciousness knows
Itself to be immaterial in substance, but It
also takes form (manifests) as your
physical body and the material world
around you. Thus, you may describe
yourself as being both immaterial
(spiritual) and material (physical) at the
same time.*

List ten things you want in your life that you do not yet have. List
the things that first come to your mind.

1. _____

2. _____

3. _____

4. _____

5. _____

6. _____

7. _____

8. _____

9. _____

10. _____

"Ideas are the primal, original source of everything that manifests in visible form. In our universe, we turn ideas into material form. Visualization is a powerful tool for doing so."

Pick the one thing that is most important to you. Close your eyes and see it in your mind. If it is an object, see its color, its shape. If it is a place or a goal, see how your surroundings look, how other people look, where you are. Visualize every detail. Write or sketch what you see.

"The practice of creative visualization is not idle daydreaming or wishful thinking... It is focused imagining, with the power of your will and persistence behind it."

"If you give equal time to images contrary to your objective, it would be like trying to dig a hole and fill it up at the same time."

What sorts of ideas and visualizations do you have that go against what you want? Write or sketch them here.

Are you limiting yourself by being "realistic"? How?

_____

_____

_____

_____

_____

_____

_____

"To be 'realistic' is to know that all visible manifestations follow the ideas and images you hold in your mind."

Now visualize not just what you want, but how you intend to get it. Do not limit yourself. Write or sketch what you see.

"Now that you are aware that visualization is a powerful part of the creative process, use this wonderful tool to lend momentum to achieving your goals! Allow only those images in your mind that support you and others, and see how quickly things change."

4   *Becoming One With Your Silent Master*

SEVEN STEPS TO INNER POWER

This chapter will teach you how to identify with your Silent Master, to claim Its power and intelligence, to become One with It. Your Silent Master Consciousness is already a part of you. Your creative power will unfold and develop automatically as you begin using these seven principles, because they will cause you to think as your Silent Master does.

Remember Silent Master Image III:

YOUR THOUGHTS CREATE REALITY

Your Silent Master Consciousness knows Itself to be immaterial in substance, but It also takes form (manifests) as your physical body and the material world around you. Thus, you may describe yourself as being both immaterial (spiritual) and material (physical) at the same time.

How is your physical world created by your thoughts? Can you think of an example in your own life?

_____

_____

_____

_____

_____

_____

Body and Mind as One

"Simply to know that your body and your personal world around you are created by thought, emotion, and visualization does much to help you take creative control of your life. Certainly this is the starting point."

"Just as you discipline your mind (your mental and spiritual thinking), you must discipline your body (your physical action) to conform to your mental objectives."

What influence do you have on your physical world?

_____

_____

_____

_____

_____

What influence do you have over your thoughts?

_____

_____

_____

_____

_____

"You will have a natural inclination to take physical actions that are in accord with your thinking."

In what ways do your actions hinder your goals?

_____

_____

_____

_____

In what ways do your actions support your goals?

_____

_____

_____

_____

_____

Draw or describe how you physically look (short, tall, fat, slim, athletic, couch potato, strong) in the space below.

Next to the picture, list mental and emotional traits you have (disciplined, lazy, go-getter, dependent, independent).

"Your bodily actions must be at one with your mental efforts."

Compare your picture and your list of traits. How does your physical body relate to your mental condition?

_____

_____

_____

_____

_____

_____

Which mental or emotional traits support your body?

_____

_____

_____

How does your body support you mentally and emotionally?

_____

_____

_____

How are your thoughts in harmony or disharmony with your body?

_____

_____

_____

If you want to change, what things do you need to change?

☯ In your body?

_____

_____

_____

_____

_____

☯ In your mind?

_____

_____

_____

Have you ever felt your body was outside of your control? When?

_____

_____

_____

_____

_____

_____

_____

_____

_____

What mentally and emotionally was going on in your life at that time?

_____

_____

_____

_____

_____

_____

_____

_____

_____

_____

"If you insist on regarding your body as separate from your mind, this belief will take form as your body being outside your control. Your belief of separateness will cause your body to seemingly have a separate 'mind' of its own, and then it can say things like "I am ill; I am too weak to do this or that; I can't; I won't..." and so on. This mistaken belief of a separate mind and body does not change reality, but it certainly denies it and you lose your power."

"Your body is a holy place and deserving of your utmost love, care, and respect."

How do you mentally feel when you physically feel strong?

_____

_____

_____

_____

_____

_____

_____

_____

"You can look at your body and gain insight into the quality of your thinking; and you can look at your thinking to determine how to shape and direct your body. When your thoughts are healthy, your body reflects this condition. When you're ill, it may be helpful to examine your state of mind or the state of your beliefs to locate the cause of your illness."

How do you mentally feel when you are physically ill?

_____

_____

_____

_____

_____

_____

_____

_____

Is your body at one with your mind? Why or why not?

_____

_____

_____

_____

_____

_____

_____

_____

To change this situation, I must change...

❂ Physically:

_____

_____

❂ Emotionally:

_____

_____

❂ Mentally:

_____

_____

❂ Spiritually:

_____

_____

"Your body and mind, then, are designed to act as one at all times. This may take much focus, determination, and concentration on your part. For instance, you may set a goal of winning a marathon race. Your mind says, "This is an important priority; I want to win; I want to use all my spare time building up my speed and endurance by practicing every day." If you nevertheless insist on partying often to late hours, eating improperly, skipping workouts 'just this one time,' accepting frivolous invitations... how likely are you to succeed under these circumstances?"

"Remember, what you do with every moment of now is all that matters. There will never be a tomorrow to realize your goals."

Truth

Truth is Self Discovery! As you develop the habit of regarding your body and life experiences as pictures of your thinking, you will certainly begin to learn something about yourself. Isn't this what we call the moment of truth? Now answer these questions again, based on what you have been discovering about yourself.

What strengths have you discovered in yourself? List ten.

1. _____
2. _____
3. _____
4. _____
5. _____
6. _____
7. _____
8. _____
9. _____
10. _____

What weaknesses have you discovered in yourself? List ten.

1. _____
2. _____
3. _____
4. _____
5. _____
6. _____
7. _____
8. _____
9. _____
10. _____

Which list was easier to write, your strengths or your weaknesses?

Remember Silent Master Image I:

YOU ARE ONE OF A KIND

Your Silent Master is your Real Self, your original Self... It is your eternal Selfhood that exists apart from your brain (which is a sensory processor only) and the personality traits imposed on you from your environment.

List ten traits that your family and friends used to describe you when you were growing up.

1. _____

2. _____

3. _____

4. _____

5. _____

6. _____

7. _____

8. _____

9. _____

10. _____

Do these traits describe who you really are? Are any of these traits the complete opposite of your true self? Which ones?

_____

_____

_____

_____

"The culture you are raised in also affects your self-concept. The same person could develop a different view of himself if he were raised in tribal Africa or in the Soviet Union, because he would be exposed to different religious, political, and social ideas; all these shape how we see our place in the world."

How do you think your culture has influenced you?

_____

_____

_____

_____

_____

_____

_____

_____

_____

Have you listened more to outside sources than to yourself in forming your self-image? Explain your answer.

_____

_____

_____

_____

_____

_____

_____

_____

_____

What do you say about yourself in the following situations? Write down the first thing that comes to your mind.

☯ Looking in the mirror:

Example: "I am overweight."

_____

_____

☯ Looking at other people:

Example: "I'm good at making friends."

_____

_____

☯ Hearing your own voice:

Example: "My high, wavering voice gives away my self-doubt."

_____

_____

☯ Hearing other people speak to you:

Example: "I know how to get people to open up."

_____

_____

☯ Walking up a steep flight of stairs:

Example: "I am out of shape."

_____

_____

"There is another factor that causes you to lose touch with yourself: Relying solely on the evidence of your five material senses to tell you who you are."

☯ Lifting something heavy:

Example: "I am healthy and strong."

_____

_____

☯ Smelling, tasting, or touching something that makes you react emotionally (describe what you react to as well):

Example: "The smell of food reminds me that I have no willpower."

_____

_____

Which of these sensory-based beliefs about yourself are false or within your power to change?

_____

_____

_____

_____

_____

_____

_____

"Whether good or bad, these images and sensations from outside impress us with a feeling of hard reality, making us feel we can't change things... But because all outside images were first created as thoughts, new thoughts can create new images."

What is impressed on you?

_____

_____

_____

_____

What do you want to express?

_____

_____

_____

_____

_____

_____

_____

_____

_____

"The truth is, strength is one of the ideas in the Silent Master Consciousness; therefore you can express that idea. The key word is 'express' which literally means to 'press outward.' "

In the space below, describe or draw who you are and who you want to become based on your journey so far. Remember: you are not limited!

"The Truth is that the only ideas about you that are real are ideas that express beauty, power, dominion, strength, love, wisdom, clarity, and perfection... As you identify yourself with these ideas, see how easily you move from one stage of development to another, setting higher and higher goals, because, in truth, you are not limited."

Purity

"If our Real Selves know only love and health, where do hate, illness, greed, lust, revenge, and all other negatives come from? The answer is this: Negative concepts are not ideas at all; they ate the absence of an idea, the unreal shadows of something real... When you experience them, they are only pointing to a real idea you are not expressing. This means there is nothing standing in the way of your purity."

We routinely wash our bodies because we have a natural desire to remove anything foreign from our physical being. So, when we reject foreign, limited concepts about ourselves, we are expressing purity.

List the ten weaknesses you discovered in the second exercise under "Truth." For each, describe the real idea you are not expressing. For example:

Weakness	Unexpressed Real Idea
Greed	The power to create all I need out of my own ideas
Hate	Love, to fill the void, as in "I love certain qualities he does not express."
Fear	The power of knowing who I am in truth

	Weakness	Unexpressed Real Idea
1.	_____	_____
2.	_____	_____
3.	_____	_____
4.	_____	_____
5.	_____	_____
6.	_____	_____
7.	_____	_____
8.	_____	_____
9.	_____	_____
10.	_____	_____

For each unexpressed real idea, list an action you can take to express that idea and eliminate the weakness.

1. _____

2. _____

3. _____

4. _____

5. _____

6. _____

7. _____

8. _____

9. _____

10. _____

"Your mental immune system is your mental purity, the constant attention you give to which thoughts are Self (the Silent Master) and which are not-Self (negative and limited)."

Take a long look at yourself in the biggest mirror you can find. How do you honestly feel about this person?

_____

_____

_____

_____

_____

_____

_____

_____

Love

"Before you can express love, you must find love. You must know love within yourself before you can express it. You must love yourself before you can give it to another."

How much do you love yourself, on a scale of one to ten?

1   2   3   4   5   6   7   8   9   10

The last time someone told you they loved you, how did you feel?
Were you surprised? Did you feel you didn't deserve their love?

_____

_____

_____

_____

_____

_____

_____

_____

How do you think this relates to your feelings about yourself?

_____

_____

_____

_____

_____

_____

_____

_____

Review the strengths you listed in the first exercise under "Truth." With these strengths in mind, close your eyes for a few minutes and see yourself as what you want to become, as fulfilling your true potential. Draw or describe what you see.

"When you recognize or experience the truth about yourself, you automatically feel love, because love is a part of your true consciousness and true ideas."

List the qualities and potential you have for which you are grateful. Does this change how you feel about yourself?

_____

_____

_____

_____

_____

_____

_____

_____

"Experiencing gratitude is a simple way to connect with the love imparted to you and every idea in the universe. The direct experience of the consciousness of love is gratitude. Gratitude is the process of recognizing what is true. Gratitude is an act of awareness. Without awareness, there is no recognition of anything, and, therefore, no love of anything."

What else evokes in you a feeling of gratitude? Special people?
Nature? Music?

_____

_____

_____

_____

_____

_____

_____

Have you ever done anything that made someone really happy?
Maybe you secretly put a flower on someone's windshield, or bought
your friend that CD they have been wanting. How did it make you
feel?

_____

_____

_____

_____

_____

_____

_____

_____

_____

Remember:

VI
YOU ARE COMPLETE, PEACEFUL, AND FULFILLED

*Your Silent Master expresses
completeness, fulfillment, harmony, peace,
joy, and love, and imparts these qualities
to everything It creates.*

Have you ever acted in a way that wasn't consistent with your true
self? Describe the situation and how you felt.

Loyalty

_____

_____

_____

_____

_____

_____

_____

*"The momentum of love
is the essence of loyalty,
so loyalty is the result of
perpetuating, reinforcing,
and expressing your real
self by loving it... There
is no greater way to love
your real self than by
being It. That is loyalty."*

Have you ever stood up for your beliefs even though others
disagreed with you? Describe the situation and how you felt.

_____

_____

_____

_____

_____

_____

_____

_____

Which of these situations do you regret more? Why?

_____

_____

_____

_____

_____

_____

_____

_____

Loyalty to Your Goals

List the most important goals you want to achieve or changes you want to make in your life. Circle whether you have been loyal to each goal and state your reason why or why not.

Goal	Have You Been Loyal?			Why or Why Not?
_____	Yes	Somewhat	No	_____
_____	Yes	Somewhat	No	_____
_____	Yes	Somewhat	No	_____
_____	Yes	Somewhat	No	_____
_____	Yes	Somewhat	No	_____
_____	Yes	Somewhat	No	_____
_____	Yes	Somewhat	No	_____
_____	Yes	Somewhat	No	_____
_____	Yes	Somewhat	No	_____

When you are disloyal to your goals, how do you feel about yourself? Why?

_____

_____

_____

_____

_____

_____

"If you act with your body and mind as one, if you know the truth about yourself, if you express purity and love, you have done much to achieve your goal. It is at this point you must exercise loyalty to your cause so you bring your vision to completion, so you do not give up, turn back, regress, or undermine yourself."

List ten things you can do to be more loyal to yourself and your goals.

1. _____

2. _____

3. _____

4. _____

5. _____

6. _____

7. _____

8. _____

9. _____

10. _____

"Aren't you deserving of your own loyalty? How much loyalty are you willing to show your Silent Master, the infinite part of you constantly standing ready, like a friend, to give you everything?"

What does sacrifice mean to you? Is it a positive or negative idea to you? Why?

Sacrifice

_____

_____

_____

_____

"When you have a goal that is a priority, and when you commit your total loyalty to this cause, you will undoubtedly make decisions about competing priorities in your life."

"When your Silent Master gives you a desire, It will never ask you to sacrifice something you need. That is contrary to Its nature of love."

Review the goals you said you were not loyal to in the exercise under "Loyalty." Is there something you are doing that is directly getting in the way of your reaching one of your goals? What is it?

_____

_____

_____

_____

_____

_____

"When you find yourself at a crossroads and you must make a choice, look closely to see if the so-called sacrifice is really a loss."

Weigh the advantages and disadvantages of sacrificing the action that gets in the way of your goal. For example, this person is deciding whether to continue eating ice cream when going out with friends:

	Advantage	Disadvantage
Sacrificing	I will reach my weight goal much more easily because I will eat less.	I might feel embarrassed eating jello instead.
NOT Sacrificing	I get to eat whatever I want.	If my eating habits stay the same, my weight will stay the same.

Fill in the following table for the action that gets in the way of your goal:

	Advantage	Disadvantage
Sacrificing		
NOT Sacrificing		

Based on what you wrote in the table, is the sacrifice worth it? Why or why not?

_____

_____

_____

_____

_____

List five goals in your life that you have already accomplished. For each goal, write down how long it took to achieve that goal.

Goal	How Long?
1. _____	_____
2. _____	_____
3. _____	_____
4. _____	_____
5. _____	_____

List five goals you have not accomplished that you think will take a long time to achieve.

Goal	How Long?
1. _____	_____
2. _____	_____
3. _____	_____
4. _____	_____
5. _____	_____

How important are these goals? Are they more important than your short-term goals?

_____

_____

_____

"When we discussed increase and decrease with the yin-yang symbol, we said that every decrease carries with it the seed of some new increase... So, even a real sacrifice is not ever really a loss. It is preparation for a new condition."

Patience

"Let's assume you have a goal. You've acted with your body and mind as one, you have expressed truth, purity, love, loyalty, and you've sacrificed all mental and physical obstacles. Yet the goal has yet to be realized. What's left? Patience is the last step in this creative process. It is here that some impatient people may allow all their hard work to backslide."

83

Has impatience ever caused you to give up on a goal, or to interfere with it being realized in some way? What happened, and how did you feel?

_____

_____

_____

_____

_____

Have you ever been glad you waited longer than you expected for a goal to be realized? What happened, and how did you feel?

_____

_____

_____

_____

_____

"The laws of manifestation that govern our being are absolute. We must have the patience and trust to let them work."

Did you learn something about timing in life from this experience? What was it?

_____

_____

_____

_____

_____

Describe or sketch your most important goal in the space below.

"One of nature's most beautiful symbols of patience is the transformation—the metamorphosis—of the caterpillar into a butterfly, when the outward picture of the caterpillar's 'beingness' changes drastically from one form to another... If you desire to make a change as great as this, consider how the quality of patience is essential."

"True patience is knowing the truth and expecting the truth to manifest... When you express this true patience, you think as your Silent Master thinks. You keep the power turned on as you wait knowingly for the manifestation to appear at its appointed time."

How long are you willing to wait for this goal to be realized? One year? Two years? Five years? Ten years? Longer? Is it worth any time you might have to wait?

_____

_____

_____

Summary: Learning from Each Other

"Unlike the caterpillar, usually we do not make our transformation in the darkness of a private space... Our transformation is worked out in the world classroom. Much of our learning will be out in the open, composed of many small actions that will, step by step, and moment by moment, create changes just as startling as the caterpillar's transformation."

Describe situations you encounter frequently in which each of the Seven Steps to Inner Power can help you in your relationships with other people.

☯ Body and Mind as One

Example: "If my mind and body were one, I could listen to my spouse instead of letting my mind wander."

_____

_____

_____

☯ Truth

Example: "If I expressed my true feelings, my children would know I care about them."

_____

_____

_____

☯ Purity

Example: "If I stopped being jealous of my more successful co-worker and believed in myself, there would be less tension in the office, and my boss just might notice how much more productive I am."

_____

_____

_____

"Our actions are guaranteed to affect others. Because we are not alone in this world, much of our learning about ourselves comes from our interaction with others. Our relationships are our teachers. We learn from each other."

☯ Love

Example: "If I loved myself more, I wouldn't scare away potential partners by being so needy."

_____

_____

_____

● Loyalty

Example: "If I faithfully worked out every day, I might get my out of shape friend excited enough to join me."

_____

_____

_____

● Sacrifice

Example: "If I quit smoking, I would present a better example of a healthy lifestyle to my children."

_____

_____

_____

● Patience

Example: "If I allowed new employees in my department to take longer to get up to speed, they would be happier and more productive in the long run."

_____

_____

_____

"When you're being the best person you can be, don't be surprised if you find others transforming along with you!"

5 *Your Silent Master in Action*

PHYSICAL TRAINING IS LIFE TRAINING

Jung SuWon training has a physical form, but the tools necessary to overcome physical challenges apply to every kind of challenge, because Body and Mind are One. In this chapter, you will learn how to use these tools to bring about the victory you seek.

"He can do, she can do, why not me?" Anyone can apply this simple truth to any situation, but, most important, you can apply it just as well as anyone else! How would you apply this phrase to...

❂ Your career?

_____

_____

❂ Your relationships?

_____

_____

❂ Your health and fitness?

_____

_____

❂ Your spiritual development?

_____

_____

Overcoming Limitation

"Those victories you've seen others attain? You can too! Why not you? Too many people shortchange themselves, discount themselves with too much fear and self-doubt. You have power!"

Mental Warfare

"You are not a warrior only because you learn to physically fight. The seeker is a warrior also because the 'not-self' traits you may have identified as 'you' are not necessarily easy to relinquish. In fact, most of us experience a struggle of one degree or another every time we challenge a weakness in ourselves."

State a goal or a change you desire that has been very difficult for you to make happen.

_____

_____

_____

_____

_____

_____

_____

List five of your thoughts or actions that have interfered with this goal or change.

1. _____

2. _____

3. _____

4. _____

5. _____

"Keep in mind, as we discussed in the section on Purity in chapter four, that your weaknesses are 'shadows' of your real characteristics... The war can be won by gently embodying the real idea about yourself... 'Gently' doesn't mean 'weakly,' however."

Think of a way you can gently but persistently counter each of these thoughts or actions.

1. _____

2. _____

3. _____

4. _____

5. _____

Knowing that you are not limited and that you have the power to overcome your weaknesses and change your environment, how do you see your life now?

"You are not limited."

Are you closer to your true self than you thought? Why?

_____

_____

_____

_____

_____

Does it now seem easier to get there? How?

_____

_____

_____

_____

_____

Have you learned new things about yourself that you never knew before? What are they?

_____

_____

_____

_____

_____

Observing Reality

"How do you observe? By being here, now, so that you are undistracted by thoughts of the future or the past (which don't exist anyway)."

Your ability to observe is a powerful, essential weapon in self-defense. It can help you avoid or escape physical, verbal, emotional, mental, and spiritual assaults on your being.

Remember a time when you got into an argument with someone. How did the argument start?

_____

_____

_____

_____

_____

Did you see it coming? Why or why not? Was your mind elsewhere?

_____

_____

_____

_____

_____

_____

What were your thoughts and feelings during and after the argument? Did emotions such as pride or resentment get in the way of your seeing the situation clearly?

_____

_____

_____

_____

_____

What emotions and attitudes did the other person have? Try to remember as many details as you can.

_____

_____

_____

_____

_____

What could you have done to avoid the argument? Be creative.

_____

_____

_____

_____

_____

What could you have done to change the outcome in a way that resolved the conflict more effectively? Again, be creative.

_____

_____

_____

_____

_____

"Focusing on the present moment is truly observing reality. The only time that can happen is now."

In the space below, draw or describe what you are aware of right now, in yourself and your surroundings. Observe as much as you can.

Do some of the things you are aware of in this exercise surprise you? Why or why not?

_____

_____

_____

_____

In a meditation, we think about what we care about. Whether the meditation is formal or informal, there are two steps:

1. Affirm to yourself that you and your Silent Master are One, and expect that the necessary information (or serenity, or clarity, or cleansing, or whatever) will manifest.

2. Quiet your mind, so that all the clamoring thoughts and feelings are put aside.

Moving Meditation

Moving with your Body and Mind as One is a moving meditation.

Describe how each of the following activities could be a moving meditation. In each case, how would you focus your mind? Feel free to be creative.

"You may ask, 'If that's what a moving meditation is, what about when I'm balancing my checkbook, or cleaning house, or building a cabinet?' If so, you have grasped my meaning."

☯ Getting ready for work in the morning

Example: "I am clearing away yesterday's concerns and focusing on what I want to accomplish today."

_____

_____

_____

☯ Working at your job

Example: "I am focusing on my goals for the day and not allowing anything to distract me."

_____

_____

_____

☯ Cleaning the house

Example: "I am cleaning away the old and focusing on a new beginning."

_____

_____

_____

☯ Engaging in sports

Example: "I am totally focused on the present moment and aware of all my surroundings—the field, the other players, the ball."

_____

_____

_____

☯ Driving

Example: "I am maintaining a calm state of mind as I patiently and persistently continue on my journey."

_____

_____

_____

"Any activity that brings you into a deeper communion with your real self is a moving meditation, whether it's playing the piano, walking in the woods, smelling flowers in the garden—whatever gives you this peaceful unity."

☯ Cooking a meal

Example: "I am expressing my love for the people who will receive this meal, including myself."

_____

_____

_____

☯ Eating a meal

Example: "I am focusing on loving myself as I nourish my body."

_____

_____

_____

☯ Sharing affection with your significant other

Example: "I am focusing completely on this moment together, on the beauty of who you are and the joy you bring to my life."

_____

_____

_____

☯ Playing with your kids

Example: "I am expressing my gratitude to you, because you remind me of how much joy there is in life."

_____

_____

_____

☯ Singing or dancing

Example: "I am one with the music as I send this loving message from my heart to the world."

_____

_____

_____

6 Communing With Your Silent Master

MEDITATION

This chapter teaches you the basic practice of meditation—how to directly experience your Silent Master. The possibilities are infinite.

In the last chapter we discussed moving meditation, how to bring your Body and Mind as One in all your activities. You can informally meditate anywhere and at any time. Sometimes, meditation is simply closing your eyes and taking a few deep breaths before plunging into the next challenge.

Before you meditate formally, list some questions you want to pose to your Silent Master. You can pose one of these questions in step 12 of the formal meditation described below.

Informal Meditation

Formal Meditation

"Formal meditation can be one of the most satisfying, rewarding aspects of your life."

_____

_____

_____

_____

_____

_____

_____

_____

_____

_____

Here are the steps for formal meditation from *Seven Steps to Inner Power*:

1. Sit calmly on the floor or on a flat pillow. If you use a pillow, try to keep one especially for that purpose, one you do not use for anything else. If you need to purchase a pillow, silk or cotton ones are recommended.

2. Bend your right leg and place your foot under your right thigh.

3. Bend your left leg and lift the left foot onto your right thigh. If this hurts, don't force it; just do the best you can. Your legs should now be crossed with the right on the bottom and the left on top.

4. Bend your body forward, arch your back, and then straighten up.

5. Place your right hand, palm facing up, gently on your lap.

6. Place your left hand, palm facing up, on your right hand and bring your thumbs together. The thumbs should be just barely touching, as if you were holding a sheet of paper between them.

7. Straighten your neck. Your head should be level, not up or down, and your ear lobes in line with your shoulders.

8. Close your eyes gently.

9. Close your mouth and place your tongue on the roof of your mouth.

10. Breathe in deeply through your nose, hold your breath as long as you can comfortably, and then exhale slowly and softly. Your breathing should be gentle and quiet; someone sitting next to you should not be able to hear you breathe. You will probably notice your heart slows down as well.

11. Let any worries or concerns or clamoring thoughts and feelings flow away. Remember, initially your conscious mind feels uncomfortable when you ask it to suspend its habitual thinking processes (or more often, worrying processes). It wants to keep thinking and will try to do so. Just continue breathing, however, and refuse to pay attention to intrusive thoughts and feelings. Let them go, let them pass. If necessary, "tell them" you'll pay attention to them later, but not now (usually they go away when they have this "reassurance"). Right now, you want to strive for the most pristine purity and clarity of consciousness you can; and to do that, you must suspend your customary thinking processes. Eventually, you will feel your mind start to clear.

12. Now in this stillness, pose your question, your problem, your visualization, or whatever. Ask. Ask in whatever way feels right. Your Silent Master is listening.

13. Relax your mind, and determine now to let all thoughts flow to you freely. These thoughts will have a different feeling altogether than the clamoring ones you may have had in the beginning. These thoughts are messengers of one sort or another, responses swimming into your awareness as a result of your meditation. Do not become attached to any of them. Let them come and go as they will. Pay attention to them, but do not force yourself to analyze or think about them. You can analyze later, because your conscious mind is well equipped to do so.

The first question I asked you to pose in *Seven Steps to Inner Power* was "Who Am I?" My purpose in giving you the teachings of Jung SuWon is to help you extend your vision of yourself. It is at this point that you have enough tools to ask this question again. This time, however, I encourage you to pose this question to your Silent Master in formal meditation.

When you reach step 12 in the meditation procedure just given, ask "Who am I?" This question is the complete meditation. You ask the question with all your feeling, lovingly, and sincerely. You may repeat the question several times, slowly, and with full concentration. Then, you listen... Listen until you have the knowing that you've listened long enough, even if you feel you haven't received any answer. You have; the answer will begin to manifest in many different ways for as long as you continue to repeat the meditation.

This meditation requires much repetition and patient listening. The understanding that results from it often doesn't happen all at once. The growing awareness can be so subtle that you don't realize you're getting it until you have it.

Perform this meditation for several days. On the next few pages, draw or describe your experiences.

Who am I?

"The question, 'Who Am I?', when posed to your own Silent Master, is one of the simplest, yet one of the most profound meditations you can undertake. You are asking your real self to show you that It is You."

"Although you know that you are of this creation, you know you exist apart from it. You know that you are the Sun behind the sun, that your fire burns eternally behind everything that is known as time, and everything that is known as place, and everything that is known as the Universe. And your fire is infinite Love, Awareness, Truth, Consciousness, which speaks to you and says, 'Before you are, I Am. And I Am You.'"

Acknowledgments

Today I am still a student as well as a Grandmaster. Every person who comes into my life teaches me. Each one is a unique individual with something special to give the world. I thank God for the opportunity to help my students uncover their true strengths and abilities.

My special thanks go to master instructors Scott H. Salton and Michael B. Fell; senior instructors Thomas C. Saunders and Mark E. Amador; instructors Erika A. Sommers, Kristina S. Williams, and Chase S. Lang; and junior instructor Jacklyn Marie for putting forward their dedication, support, and commitment.

Finally, I want to thank all my students who put their energy together as *one universal mind, one strength, one power, and one healing force*. With the power of this unity, there are no obstacles we cannot overcome.

Thank you all.

About the Author

Grandmaster Tae Yun Kim is a world-renowned ki energy master and one of the highest-ranked martial artists in the world.

Grandmaster Kim is the first female master of martial arts ever to come out of Korea. She began at the age of seven, learning ancient, traditional methods of Ki energy development in the solitude of the mountains.

Grandmaster Kim is the CEO of Lighthouse, a successful computer company in California's Silicon Valley. She is also a dynamic lecturer and motivational speaker, addressing both business and personal success.

Most fundamentally, however, Grandmaster Kim is a teacher. She works with people from all walks of life to help them overcome their difficulties and achieve their dreams.

Grandmaster Kim demonstrates the power of what she teaches in all areas of her own life. At 52, she looks easily half her age and radiates beauty, health, serenity, compassion, and a zest for life.

Product Catalog

Order Code: B: Book, V: Video, A: Audio

B101, $9.95 **Seven Steps to Inner Power** — Provides an accelerated sampling of Grandmaster Tae Yun Kim's philosophy and teachings on how to succeed in the modern day world. Her motto, 'He can do, She can do, why not me!' embodies her belief that every person has an incredible power just waiting to be tapped!

B102, $10.95 **The Silent Master** — By following the Silent Master within, you can overcome any obstacle and rise above limitation. Each chapter outlines a different aspect of self-discovery and offers a specific lesson designed to put the concepts into action.

B103, $14.95 **Secrets to Managing Your Energy: The Ki to Life** — Grandmaster Kim explains ki energy in terms of your environment, your relationships with others, your health, and your ability to create the life you've always wanted.

V201, $29.95 **The Seven Principles of Inner Power: Shim Gong Video** — Grandmaster Kim demonstrates the *Seven Steps to Inner Power* in this inspiring action-packed video. Includes interviews from students who have used these principles to achieve outstanding results on the training floor and their lives.

V203, $29.95 **Reaching Beyond the Ordinary: Nae Gong Video** — Grandmaster Kim demonstrates five ways of thinking that will improve your physical performance. This is the groundwork for the *Seven Steps to Inner Power*, presented in a video full of practical philosophy and spectacular action.

V204, $39.95 **Ki Rhythms Video** — This video takes you through step by step energy forms that help to reduce stress, focus on your goals, overcome obstacles and increase your energy.

A301, $12.95 **Be Free** — Virtually everyone has something that prevents them from being their best. Whether it's lack of confidence, fear, stress, anger, jealousy, or another negative emotion, we must learn to let go and learn to Be Free.

A302, $12.95 **Rising Above** — Listen to the sounds of nature as Grandmaster Kim takes you through an inspiring meditation exercise designed to relieve stress and develop motivation.

A303, $12.95 **Be An Original** — Follow Grandmaster Kim as she leads you through the process of eliminating self-doubt and lack of confidence. Develop a greater feeling of self-worth. Yes you can do it!

A304, $12.95 **Ocean Magic** — Grandmaster Kim uses the power of the ocean along with a centuries-old meditation technique to produce an extremely relaxing and revitalizing mental state you can experience time and time again.

A305, $12.95 **Grandmaster's Song** — An instrumental music track inspired by Grandmaster Kim is designed to release anxiety, relieve stress and enhance clear thinking.

A306, $12.95 **New Dimensions** — A radio talk show broadcast worldwide on the New Dimensions radio show. A dynamic one hour seminar with Grandmaster Tae Yun Kim on the topic of rising above your environment and the *Seven Steps to Inner Power*.

A307, $49.95 **Ki Energy Set of 6 Audio Tapes** — This meditation series is a collection of beautiful music sung by Grandmaster Kim. Designed to recharge your energy while meditating, working at a desk, preparing a meal, driving a car, relaxing, or before you go to sleep. You may notice that certain melodies will help you focus and energize your day.

A310, $24.95 **Seven Steps to Inner Power Book on Tape** — You can read *Seven Steps to Inner Power* or listen to it! No matter who you are, no matter where you are, no matter what obstacles and limitations exist around you at this moment, you can change your life, your health, and your state of mind completely. Through these three powerful tapes, you can decide who you want to become.

A311, $12.95 **Whisper to Your Soul** —Spread your wings and soar as Grandmaster Kim's flute takes you on a journey of peaceful tranquillity. This is the first time this audio has ever been released to the public. Composed and performed by a Ki Energy Master, these melodies are ideal for accompanying meditation, massage, or as a soothing background for any environment.

These products are available from:

NORTHSTAR

119 Minnis Circle, Milpitas, CA 95035

1-800-565-8713 Fax (408) 942-0925

www.gonorthstar.com

Order Form

Item#	Qty	Description	Unit Price	Total

Charge: Visa / MC / AMEX EXP: #: DATE::	Subtotal	
Signature: Name (print):	CA add applicable tax	
Address:	*S/H (US only)	
City / State / Zip	TOTAL	

* Shipping/handling: $5.00 for the first item or set, add $2.00 for each additional item or set. International orders: S/H costs handled on a per order basis.

Make checks payable to:

NORTHSTAR

119 Minnis Circle, Milpitas, CA 95035

1-800-565-8713 Fax (408) 942-0925

www.gonorthstar.com